Nothing Is for Free

by Margo Sorenson

Mange tak to all of my Scandinavian family and friends who shared the gift of their heritage.

M. S.

Cover Illustration: Maureen A. Scullin
Inside Illustration: Michael A. Aspengren

Text © 1996 by Perfection Learning® Corporation.
Printed in the United States of America. For information, contact Perfection Learning® Corporation, Logan, Iowa 51546.
Printed in U.S.A.

Contents

	Background Summary	5
1.	Forced to Go	7
2.	How Long Do They Have to Stay Here?	13
3.	New School Problems	19
4.	Frustration for Ike	26
5.	Ambush	35
6.	Harald Opens His Mouth	43
7.	Father's Job	50
8.	No New Skates?	58
9.	Who Did It?	64
10.	Family Sticks Together	71

Background Summary

Millions of people were out of work. Banks ran out of money and closed down. Companies shut down. Farmers went broke. They lost their land and their homes. Grown men lost their jobs and sold apples on the street. People stood in lines just to get bread to eat. Hard times hit everyone.

What was the name of this time in United States history? It was called the Great Depression. Everyone in the United States was affected in one way or another. The Great Depression began in 1929 when the stock market crashed. Suddenly, companies that had been successful were worth nothing at all. Many of them had borrowed too much money. This caused a ripple effect. The Great Depression lasted for a long time—more than 10 years. It wasn't until the United States entered World War II in 1941 that the economy started to improve.

6

1

Forced to Go

Ike stared at his father. He couldn't believe what he had just heard.

Father sighed. He stamped his muddy boots on the doormat.

"*What?* We have to move? *Why?*" Ike almost shouted at his father.

Father walked slowly into their tiny kitchen. His shoulders slumped. What's wrong with him? Ike wondered. What's happening?

Father looked at Mother. Then he looked at the floor. Mother stood at the stove, stirring. Her mouth was firm.

"Why?" Ike asked again. "We've always lived here! This is where my friends are."

Father sighed. "Ike," he began. "You know times are bad. Especially here in North Dakota."

Father sat down heavily. He looked at Mother again and shrugged his shoulders.

Ike frowned. He was tired of hearing about how bad times were. It was the 1930s—the Great Depression. Everybody in America was going broke. He knew his family didn't have any money. His parents made that very clear every time he asked for something.

Mother looked sad. "It's this way for many people," she said. She sighed and looked at Father.

"But why do we have to move out of Great Rock?" Ike asked. "What has changed?"

"I lost my job today," Father said. "They told me they won't need me to clean the high school any more. There is no money to pay me. The teachers will have to clean their own rooms."

Father looked uncomfortable. He stared at his hands.

"Father! No!" Ike exclaimed. "They can't fire you! You do a great job. Everyone likes you there."

Father didn't look up. Ike stared at his father's hands. They were rough. Years of hard work had hardened them.

It wasn't fair. His father worked so hard. Now he had no job.

"Your father wasn't fired," Mother said. "The school district has no money to pay him. It's happening everywhere." She walked over to the table and stood next to her husband.

Ike shook his head. He dropped down onto a chair. "But why do we have to move? Why can't you find another job here in Great Rock?"

"Right now, there are no jobs here," Father said. "Not for anyone. So no money will be coming in. I haven't been able to pay our rent. We can't stay here and not pay rent."

"But —where will we go?" Ike asked. His heart began to beat harder. No, it couldn't happen, could it? Not—not the one place he would never go. With the cousins he hated.

Mother and Father looked at each other. Mother nodded at Ike.

"Your mother's brother, Uncle Jens, has said we can live with him and his family on the farm," Father said. He leaned back in his chair. "Until times get better. Until I can get another job in town." He closed his eyes.

"No!" Ike blurted. "I hate our cousins! I won't go!" He jumped out of his chair and turned his back on Mother and Father. Ike stared out the window. Outside, the October sky was gray. Snow threatened to come soon.

"Now, Ike…" Mother began. She put her hands on her hips. Her voice started to rise.

Ike turned around. "Besides, Krista is so mean to

Anna," Ike broke in. "That's why Anna hates them too."

"What? What did you say about me?" Ike's sister, Anna, stood in the doorway. Her nine-year-old face looked worried.

"We have to move in with Harald and Krista on the farm!" Ike burst out.

Anna's eyes filled with quick tears. "We have to move?" she asked. "To the farm? And leave my school? My friends?" She looked at Mother pleadingly.

Mother walked over and put her arm around Anna.

"Don't worry, honey," she said. "It's not forever. Your father will find a job in town again. But right now, we have no choice. We have no money for rent." She squeezed Anna's shoulders. "But we'll be together. We'll be a family."

"And Uncle Jens, Aunt Mary, Krista, and Harald are family too," Father said. "They are standing behind us. We need their help," he admitted.

Ike made a face. Harald and Krista sure didn't act like family. What a couple of brats!

Mother had grown up on the farm where Uncle Jens and his family now lived. She hadn't been interested in staying on the farm. So she had sold her share to Uncle Jens a long time ago. Now Mother's brother, Uncle Jens, ran the Mogren family farm.

Ike looked at Father. Father had never wanted to take money from Mother's family. He was too proud for charity. Ike knew this must be hard on Father.

"What will you do, Father?" Ike asked. He noticed how tired his father looked.

"I will try to be of some use to Uncle Jens on the farm," Father replied. He straightened his shoulders a bit.

"Ja. Your father is a hard worker," Mother said proudly. She smiled at Father over Anna's head. "He will be a big help to Jens."

Anna stood still, Mother's arm still around her. Her face was red from crying.

"But—but my friends," she said. "My teacher!" Her eyes began to fill with tears again.

"I know, my girl," Mother said. She gave Anna's shoulders another squeeze. "And Ike has a teacher he likes this year too. One who finally understands him." She smiled at Ike.

Ike knew what she meant. He had not been in trouble for fighting this year.

"I'm very proud of you, Ike." Father gave Ike a pat on the back. "You're working on that temper of yours."

Ike grinned. What Father said was true. Miss Marsh, his teacher, was nice. She listened to him. She noticed when he was about to get angry. Then she'd talk with him. That way, he wouldn't actually punch anyone. Even though he still *felt* like doing it!

"Ja," Mother said. "I'm afraid Ike got my temper— the famous Mogren temper." She smiled at Ike. "Well," she said, "maybe at the little country school, the teacher will be good too."

Oh no! He and Anna would be going to a one-room school! That was where all the farm kids went. The farm was far out in the country. Too far from Great Rock to go to school in town.

"Ike and I will go to school together?" Anna asked hopefully. A little smile began to light up her face.

Ike frowned. He didn't mind going to school with Anna. She was a nice little sister. But that meant they would have to go to school with Harald and Krista too. Ike set his jaw. Not only would he have to *live* with his hated cousins, he would have to go to *school* with them too. And in the same room yet. He would spend almost every waking hour with those jerks.

How long would it be until Father found another job? And how could he stand living with those brats until then?

2

How Long Do
They Have to Stay Here?

A long two days had passed since Ike had found out they were moving. They'd packed their few things. Father had already driven one load out to the farm. Their little rented house in Great Rock was empty now. Just the furniture that had come with it was left.

"Good-bye, house," Anna had cried. Ike had stared at the ground. Then they all piled into the old Ford. As his father drove off, Ike turned around in the backseat. He watched the house for as long as he could. He still couldn't believe this was happening.

Father drove the old Ford up in front of the Mogren farmhouse. Ike slumped down in his seat. He didn't even want to look out.

"We're here," Mother said. She opened the car door.

Ike could tell she was trying to sound cheerful. This was hard for Mother too. She and Aunt Mary were so different. Ike knew it wasn't easy for Mother to go back to her girlhood home asking for help.

The Mogren farmhouse door opened. Uncle Jens hurried out smiling.

"Welcome, family," he said heartily. He walked across the yard to the car.

At least Uncle Jens is nice, Ike thought. Probably because he is Mother's brother.

Behind him, Ike saw Aunt Mary in the doorway. Slowly, she walked out to greet them.

"Lillie, welcome," Aunt Mary said with a smile. She gave Mother a quick hug. "Nils," she said, nodding to Father.

A frowning face popped up in the farmhouse window. Then it disappeared. Harald was spying on them as usual. What a sneak, thought Ike.

Everyone carried in the boxes and bags. It was sad to think that their whole life was packed up in a few boxes.

"Harald? Krista?" Uncle Jens called. "Where are

you?"

Ike and the rest of the Johnson family stood awkwardly in the front room. Bags and boxes lay around them. Uncle Jens looked at Aunt Mary.

"Well, where are they? Why aren't they here?" he asked. He folded his arms and frowned.

Aunt Mary sighed. Without a word, she left the room. Father looked at Mother. Mother shook her head.

"Look, I—I'm sorry," Uncle Jens said. He shrugged his shoulders.

"Don't apologize, please," Mother said. She smiled at him. "I know it's not easy for the children. They have to share their rooms. Their lives are changing. I'm sure they don't like it."

Ike couldn't believe his ears. His mother was talking about Harald and Krista. How could she feel sorry for them? Harald and Krista still had a house. They could stay in the same school. They didn't have to leave their friends. Their father had a job.

Ike frowned. Down the hall, he could hear hushed voices.

"Don't you dare!" That was Aunt Mary's voice whispering.

"I will if I want to!" Ike recognized Harald's snotty voice right away. How he'd like to bust him one right across that spoiled face of his. Too bad Harald was a year younger. His father would accuse him of picking on a younger kid.

Aunt Mary came in. She sighed and looked at Uncle Jens. Krista and Harald followed slowly behind. Harald dragged his feet. He was scowling. Krista's face was red. Her lower lip stuck out in a pout.

Ike frowned. Harald and Krista didn't look happy to have them there. Well, he wasn't happy to be there either! He'd rather stay in the barn with the animals than live with Harald. Uncle Jens and Aunt Mary were all right. But sharing a room with Harald? He shuddered. He sure hoped Father would find a job in town—and quickly.

"Children," Uncle Jens said sternly, "say hello to the family."

" 'Lo," Harald mumbled, not looking up. He scuffed his foot back and forth on the rug.

"Hello," Krista muttered, sniffling. She rubbed her nose with the back of her hand.

"Look at people when you speak to them!" Uncle Jens' voice rang out. "Welcome your family."

Harald and Krista both jumped. They looked at the Johnsons.

"He—hello," they said together.

Ike had never seen Uncle Jens angry. Relief rushed over him. Uncle Jens seemed to really want them there. At least someone did.

"Children, take Anna and Ike to your rooms. Help them get settled," Uncle Jens said.

Ike picked up his bag of clothes. He followed Harald down the hall. He'd been in Harald's room many times.

16

He never thought he'd be sharing it though.

"This is yours," Harald said, pointing to the bed in the corner. "You can have one drawer. And don't touch my stuff!" he whined. He made a face.

"I wouldn't *want* to touch your stuff," Ike said curtly.

Harald turned and left. Ike stood in the middle of the room. This was it. He felt a sinking feeling in his stomach. This was where he was going to live. How long would he have to be here?

Ike opened the bottom drawer of Harald's dresser. It was empty. Ike stuffed his shirts and pants inside. Grabbing two hangers, he hung up his one good shirt and good pair of pants. He sighed. This was going to be terrible.

When he finished, Ike walked down the hall. He could hear his parents getting settled in the spare room. He got as far as the kitchen doorway when he heard urgent whispers. Ike ducked around the corner.

"How long do they have to stay?" Aunt Mary's voice asked.

"As long as they need to, Mary," Uncle Jens answered. "Remember, they are family."

"But Harald and Krista are so unhappy, Jens," Aunt Mary said. "They don't like sharing their rooms. Krista thinks Anna is a crybaby. And that Ike is such a bully. Poor Harald!"

Ike could feel his anger pulse in his forehead. A bully, was he? Aunt Mary sure didn't know her precious Harald too well.

"Now, Mary. Harald brings some of that on himself," Uncle Jens warned. Ike could hear a kitchen chair scrape across the floor. Heavy footsteps headed toward the back door.

"And what about the extra expense?" Aunt Mary went on. "Did you forget? Times are hard for us too. Last year was not a good year on the farm. Feeding and clothing a whole extra family…"

"Mary!"

Ike started. Uncle Jens' voice was strong. "They are family, and we will help them. We will still have enough for what we really need," Uncle Jens said. He shut the back door behind him.

Ike turned around. He walked back down the hall. He was not going to go into the kitchen and face Aunt Mary. Not on his life. He stopped outside his parents' room. He leaned against the wall.

Ike closed his eyes. Aunt Mary didn't want them there either. She was worried about money too. Everyone was worried about money these days.

It seemed as if hardly anyone wanted them at the farm. But they had no choice. They had nowhere else to go.

3

New School Problems

Ike opened the door to the schoolhouse. He stamped the snow from his shoes. Beyond the little room where he stood, a doorway led to the main schoolroom. Students were coming in and out of it. They eyed him strangely.

He was standing in the storage room for the coal that burned in the school stove. There were hooks on the wall. Jackets and coats already hung on some of them.

Ike looked to his left. Harald hung up his jacket and raced inside the classroom without a backward glance.

Krista had hurried to hang up her coat too. She left Anna standing there. Now Krista was whispering with two other girls in the corner of the coal room.

Anna hung up her things and started toward the classroom. Ike watched her stop for a moment at the door to the schoolroom. Anna looked pleadingly at Krista. Krista didn't even look at her. Anna turned to Ike. She opened her mouth to say something.

"It's all right, Anna," Ike said before Anna spoke. "I'll take you in to meet the teacher."

He placed his own jacket on a hook. Taking Anna's hand, he walked into the classroom.

Rows of wooden desks with iron legs filled the room. It was like his classroom in Great Rock. The only difference was that every grade from first to eighth was in the same room.

"You must be the Johnson children." A young woman came forward, smiling. She had blonde hair piled up on her head. Her blue eyes sparkled. This was his teacher? She sure didn't look like any teacher *he'd* ever had.

"Yes," Anna said shyly. She smiled up at the teacher.

"I'm Miss Peterson," the teacher said. "You're the Mogrens' cousins, ja?" She looked at Ike.

Ike tried not to scowl. "Ja," he muttered. He didn't want to be connected with those brats.

"I see," Miss Peterson said. "I see." She looked at

Anna and Ike. "Hmmm…"

What was she thinking? Ike could see Harald out of the corner of his eye. Harald was frowning at him from across the room. There were other boys standing around too. It seemed as if everyone was listening to them. He felt his face turn warm. Why couldn't they go about their business?

He realized Miss Peterson was still looking at them. He should tell Miss Peterson their names.

"I'm Ike—Isaac, but Ike for short. This is my little sister, Anna," he said. He gave Anna's hand a squeeze.

"Nice to meet both of you," Miss Peterson said. "What grades are you in?"

"I'm in seventh grade," Ike said. He noticed some of the bigger boys elbowing each other. What were they saying? Were they going to give him a hard time? Would he have to fight to teach them a lesson? He saw Harald whisper to a boy with red hair. The boy grinned and turned to stare at Ike. Ike narrowed his eyes.

"And Anna?" Miss Peterson's voice broke into his thinking. She smiled.

Ike blinked.

"Ah—ah—Anna's in third," Ike stammered.

"I'll show you to your desks," Miss Peterson said. Ike noticed she had a dimple when she smiled. "Did you bring potatoes to bake for your lunches?" she asked.

"Yes," Ike said. That morning, he could hardly believe it when Aunt Mary told him what she was packing for their lunches. In the little country school, everyone always had a hot potato for lunch. They brought other things to eat too. Ike pulled the two potatoes from their lunch buckets.

Miss Peterson held out her hand. "Good," she said. "We'll put them on top of the stove with the others."

A black iron stove stood in the middle of the schoolroom. Its warmth filled the room. On top, about twenty potatoes sat baking in neat rows. They would be ready to eat by lunchtime.

The lessons began. Miss Peterson worked with one grade at a time. The younger children recited lessons. Some of the girls Anna's age were staring at her. Krista whispered to one of them. Then they looked at Anna. Ike frowned. Krista had better not start trouble for Anna. He would have to fix that.

Ike stared at a history book. All around him, he could hear pencils scratching across paper. He glanced over at Harald's desk. Harald made a face at him.

Ike stared hard at Harald. Finally, Harald looked down. I got him, Ike thought. He hid a grin. Ike looked at the inkwell on his desk. Wouldn't he love to push Harald's pointy nose right into it?

Miss Peterson rang the bell. The children flocked to the coal room. Coats and hats and mittens flew through the air. All bundled up, they raced outside for recess.

Ike shoved his mittened hands in his pockets. It was cold. His breath puffed out in little clouds.

Ike watched some boys gather for a game. He decided to watch for a while and then ask to join in.

Anna stood alone over by a tree. Krista was standing by the schoolhouse with two other girls. Krista whispered something to them. Then she and the two girls walked over to Anna. Ike could hear their clear voices across the school yard.

"Are those really Krista's old clothes you're wearing?" one of the girls asked Anna.

Ike could feel his blood begin to boil. How mean! Anna was silent. She looked down at the ground. Then she turned her back to hide her face. The girls with Krista laughed and walked away.

Angrily, Ike marched over to the tree. Anna's shoulders shook with her sobs.

"Hey, Anna. Don't let them bother you," Ike said. He patted Anna's shoulder. "You look nice in your dress."

"Ike, I hate it here," Anna sobbed. "No one likes me. They hate me. It's all because of Krista!"

Ike tightened his mouth. "Why don't you go back inside, Anna," he said. "Talk to Miss Peterson for a while. You'll make friends. It just takes time."

Ike led Anna across the yard to the steps. Just as he watched her go inside, a voice taunted him from behind.

"What a nice big brother you are!" a boy jeered.

Ike clenched his fists in his pockets. He whipped around. He found himself face-to-face with the red-haired boy. The boy had a rude grin on his face. Behind him, Ike saw Harald.

"Yeah? So what?" Ike growled. "Who are you? What's it to ya?"

"I'm Rolf. Rolf Bohn," the boy said, sticking out his chin. "It's anything to me I want it to be. And don't you forget it."

"Listen, Rolf," Ike said, narrowing his eyes, "don't mess with me."

"Oooooh, a tough town boy, eh?" Rolf said. "Things are different out here in the country."

That did it! Ike felt his forehead pulsing with anger. He pulled his fist out of his pocket. Then he stared at Rolf.

"*This* isn't any different, bud," Ike said, showing Rolf his fist.

Rolf took a step backward. "Just—just *you* watch it," he said weakly.

"Right," Ike snapped. Rolf looked scared. He must be one of those guys who talks tough but always backs down, Ike thought. No wonder he's friends with that jerk Harald.

Miss Peterson appeared on the steps. She rang the bell. "Time to come in, children," she called.

Students settled in their desks after hanging up their coats and jackets. Miss Peterson waited until everyone was quiet.

"As you all know, we have some new students—Ike and Anna Johnson. I want all of you to do everything you can to welcome them. I have heard some of you make unkind remarks. Let's remember that everyone is having a hard time these days."

She looked across the rows of students. Her face looked stern. "I don't want to hear of any more mean-spirited comments like I overheard this morning before school. Now, let's get to work." Miss Peterson picked up a history book. She walked over to the older students.

Ike turned his head slightly. He could see Krista two rows over. Her face was red. She had slipped down in her desk a little. Her two friends' faces were red too. Miss Peterson must have heard them talking this morning. Maybe now they would leave Anna alone.

Now all Ike had to do was handle Harald. And Rolf. Ike frowned. He was dying to fight Rolf, even though he knew he shouldn't. But Rolf was asking for it.

Ike knew he'd really disappoint Father if he started fighting again. How could he let Father down? Father had enough problems right now. He didn't need Ike to add to them.

4

Frustration for Ike

"So," Harald said with a mean smile on his face. He and Ike were walking from the barn toward the house. They had just finished milking the cows. There was so much work to do on the farm.

"So, what?" Ike said. He and his family had been living on the farm for only a week, but it seemed like forever. Ike was tired of trying to control his temper around Harald. So many times he dug his nails into his palms to keep from popping Harald right across the jaw.

"So, too bad your father can't find a job," Harald smirked. "What is he? Worthless? Lazy? Like you?" He laughed and began running up the fence line to the back door of the farmhouse.

Ike's face turned red in anger. He raced up to Harald and grabbed him by the neck of his jacket. He shoved his nose right into Harald's shocked face. He shook his other fist at him.

"Listen, you little idiot! I'm gonna make you sorry you ever..." Ike began.

Harald recovered. He jerked his face away. "No you're not!" he taunted. "If you fight me, your family will have to leave. My mother will never let you stay then."

Ike's heart pounded. What Harald said was true. He tightened his mouth and slowly loosened his grip on Harald's jacket. Harald smirked.

"You have no place to go," Harald said. "Too bad! Guess you'll just have to grin and bear it!" He jerked out of Ike's loosened hold. Then he ran to the back door laughing.

Ike stood by the fence, fuming. His heart beat furiously. He couldn't believe he actually had to take this! Father wasn't lazy. He wasn't worthless. Ike knew that.

Father was busy every day. He helped Uncle Jens with the farmwork. Now that winter was here, there were many chores. Besides taking care of animals, the harnesses needed mending. The farm machinery needed work. He had seen Father out looking at the thresher.

Father seemed to spend a lot of time reading farmers' magazines too. Ike would come into the kitchen after milking the cows and see the magazines spread out on the kitchen table. *The Farmer, Farm Stock and Home, North Dakota Farm Reporter,* and *The National Farm Journal* were some of the names. They were nothing he would ever pick up to read. But Father read them carefully.

Father also read the job ads every week in the *Walsh County News.* Ike would watch him studying the few ads. Father's forehead would crease with worry. Then he'd put the paper down with a sigh.

One day this week, Father had driven into Great Rock. Ike hoped it was for a job. But Father had returned with no job. Mother had hugged him without a word.

Why couldn't his father find a job? Was something wrong with him?

Ike began walking slowly back to the farmhouse. He knew the answer only too well. There was nothing wrong with Father. Because of the Depression, a lot of people were out of work.

He had seen the pictures in newspapers. Grown men selling apples on the streets of New York trying to earn some money. People lined up for blocks for bread and soup. Many rich had become poor.

Ike sighed and opened the back door to the kitchen. The warm air wrapped around him.

"Just what do you think you're doing?" Aunt Mary

snapped. She stood next to the stove.

Ike froze. His jaw dropped. "What—what do you mean, Aunt Mary?" he asked.

She put her hands on her hips and glared at him. "You know perfectly well what I mean," she said. "You stop bullying Harald," she said. "He's younger than you. Only bullies pick on younger boys."

Out of the corner of his eye, Ike saw Harald's grinning face in the doorway. Ike clenched his fists. This was too much to take. But he had to take it. His family had nowhere else to go.

Ike dug his fingers into his palms. He gritted his teeth. "Yes, Aunt Mary," he said. "I know. But Harald said..."

"It doesn't matter what Harald said. Words are only words," Aunt Mary replied. "There is no excuse for your behavior. I'm going to talk to your Uncle Jens. Then he'll have a talk with your father. Maybe then you'll learn. Now wash up for supper." She turned back to her work at the stove.

Fuming, Ike went to the sink. He pumped the water into the bowl and scrubbed his hands furiously. I'd like to scrub Harald's ugly face, he thought angrily.

He walked down the hall to the room he shared with Harald. He looked inside the opened door to his parents' room. Mother sat, sewing. Folds of deep red fabric spread across a table. Her head was bent over her work.

Ike wanted to tell Mother what had happened. Then

she could prepare Father. That way, Father might not be so mad.

"Mother?" Ike said. He took a step inside.

Mother looked up from her needle and thread. She smiled. "Ike, look how pretty this dress is going to be," she said. She smoothed the material with her hand.

"Uh-huh," he said. He didn't really care, but he tried to act interested. "Is it a new dress for Anna?" he asked hopefully. Maybe if she had a new dress of her own, Krista and the other girls might not tease her.

Mother looked a little sad. "No, it is for Krista," she answered.

"*Krista!*" Ike sputtered. "Krista doesn't need a new dress! Anna does!" How unfair! Here Mother was, hard at work, sewing a dress for that brat, Krista!

"Now, Ike," Mother warned. "I'm sewing it because Krista has to share her room with Anna. It is sort of a thank you." She looked at Ike. "Try to be a little more understanding."

Sure. Let the brats tease Anna. Let Harald call Father worthless. But he had to be understanding! He took a deep breath. He had to tell Mother.

"Okay, I'll try," he agreed. He sighed. "Um, Mother," Ike began.

Mother looked up from her sewing. "What is it?" she asked. "Are you in trouble? I heard Aunt Mary raise her voice in the kitchen."

"Yes. Well, sort of," Ike admitted. He told Mother the

30

story. Her face darkened. She tightened her mouth.

"Worthless and lazy?" she repeated when Ike finished. She stabbed the needle into the fabric. "That Harald is going to get into real trouble some day," she said. "But *you* are not going to let him take you down with him. You are going to hold your temper. Is that clear?" she asked in a stern voice.

Ike knew that voice. The Mogren temper again, he thought. He couldn't tell if Mother was more angry with him or Harald. But he knew his mother meant business. He knew he'd better start keeping his temper under control around Harald.

Ike sighed. "Yes, Mother," he said. "I'll try harder. I won't let Harald get my goat."

"I'll have to tell your father," Mother said. "He should know before Uncle Jens talks to him." Her voice softened a little. "He will be disappointed, you know," she said.

Ike's heart sank. Mother was right. Father was always so proud of him when he controlled himself. Now he had let Father down. He walked slowly down the hall to his room.

When Father came into the house from the barn, Mother had taken him aside. Ike knew she was talking about the fight because Ike saw the disappointment in Father's eyes. He sighed. A little later, Ike saw Father and Uncle Jens talking together in the front room.

When Father asked Ike to step out to the barn with

him, Ike knew why.

"Your Uncle Jens had a talk with me," Father began. "I understand you let your temper get the best of you, eh?" Father said, shaking his head.

Ike hung his head. He hated letting Father down.

"Ja," Ike said. "But—but you heard what Harald said, didn't you? Didn't Mother tell you?" he asked.

Father shut his eyes for a moment. "She did," he said. Then he looked at Ike. "Thank you for trying to stick up for me," Father said. "But remember, Ike. The best way to stick up for me is to not let Harald get your goat. Otherwise, he'll always win. Remember that." Father set his mouth. "These are hard times. For all of us. But fighting only makes things worse. Hear?" he asked.

Ike looked down at the ground. "Ja, Father," he said slowly.

Ike imagined Harald sneaking around listening to them. He was probably snickering to himself. Ike tightened his mouth. Control, he told himself.

Supper was halfway over before Ike could even look at Harald. He would just as soon punch him as look at him.

The supper table conversation revolved around the farm. Aunt Mary talked about baking lefse the next day, even though it wasn't a holiday.

"I'll help you!" Anna said eagerly. Aunt Mary smiled at her.

"Pass the potatoes, please," Uncle Jens said.

"Ja," Anna said. She handed the dish to Uncle Jens. "Don't eat them all, Uncle Jens," she said. "We'll need some for the lefse."

Uncle Jens smiled at her as he helped himself.

"Well," Uncle Jens said to Father. "I don't know what to do about the crops. When spring comes, I'm not sure what to plant. We had so much trouble this year."

"Ja," Father said. "You mean the dust storms?" Father took some potatoes.

"That's right," Uncle Jens said. "Some of our fields were stripped bare. We lost a lot of money." He sighed and took a drink of coffee.

Ike remembered the terrible dust storms. At the end of last summer, dry, hot dust storms had whipped across the North Dakota prairie. They barreled through Great Rock and raked all the farms. Dirt had piled up against fences like snow. Ike and Anna wore handkerchiefs over their noses and mouths to breathe. He had never seen anything like it.

"It was bad for us farmers," Uncle Jens went on. "We lost a lot of our crops to the dust storm. I'm not sure what I should be planting come spring.

"All the farmers in the area are confused. It's on everyone's minds." Uncle Jens continued. "Whatever we plant has to be hearty enough to handle the weather we've been having." He put another bite of potatoes in his mouth.

Father looked thoughtful. "No one has any ideas?" he

asked.

"Everyone has ideas," Uncle Jens said. "But no one knows if they'll work." He frowned. "We can't afford to make the wrong choices."

Ike's heart sank. If Uncle Jens was worried about money, they were all in trouble. What would Ike's family do if Uncle Jens ran out of money?

5
Ambush

Ike walked out into the gray November day. The morning sun shone weakly behind the high, thin clouds. He looked out across the frozen prairie. Farmhouses and a few trees dotted the snowy landscape. He couldn't believe they had been at the farm for almost a month.

"Hurry up, Anna," he called. "We'll be late for school."

The back door slammed. Anna and Krista tumbled out. They were bundled up in coats, scarves, and mittens.

"Ja, ja," Anna said. "We're here." Her breath puffed out in little clouds.

Ike frowned. "Where's Harald?" he asked.

"Harald said he'd be late," Krista said. "He's finishing his homework." She and Anna began crunching through the snow.

Together, all three walked down the lane. They would cut across the Ellefsons' farm. Then the school was on the next section of land.

Anna was singing a little song. Krista made a face at her. What a brat, Ike thought. He watched his boots sink into the snow. He dug his mittened hands into his pockets.

Behind him, he heard the thud of running feet.

"Wait up! Wait up!" Harald called.

Ike was tempted to speed up. He didn't like to spend any more time with Harald than he had to.

He slowed down. Harald came running up, out of breath.

"That arithmetic was harder than I thought," Harald said. He looked at Ike. "I suppose you copied yours from someone?" he jeered.

Ike bit his cheek. He had a new way to deal with Harald. He just didn't answer his taunts. That was Father's suggestion. It actually seemed to make Harald even madder. Ike hid a smile.

The four children turned in at the Ellefsons' fence. Some small sheds and a barn were clustered by the fence. They walked past the Ellefsons' barn. Ike could hear animals inside. Horses neighed and shifted in their stalls. A cow mooed.

Wham! Splat! Snowballs zinged through the air! One hit him on his leg! It was hard and it hurt.

"Hey!" Ike yelled. "Who's doing that?" He looked toward the far trees. Whoever was throwing snowballs was hiding there. "Duck down!" he told Anna and Krista. "Get back behind the barn!" He crouched down in the snow.

"Ooow!" Anna howled. "Ike! It hurts!" She rubbed her cheek with a mittened hand. She began to sob.

Ike looked at her. Her cheek was bright red. Then he looked down at what was left of the snowball. In the middle was a little rock. This wasn't just a harmless snowball fight. Someone wanted to hurt them.

"Ouch!" Krista yelled. A snowball hit her shoulder. Together, the girls ran for the safety of the barn.

Crouched next to him, Ike could hear Harald breathing. Ike narrowed his eyes. Funny, Harald hadn't gotten hit. And Ike knew why. Harald must have set up this ambush. Ike would settle with him later. Right now, he was going to fight back. He scooped up some snow and packed it tightly into a hard ball.

Ike stood up quickly and threw the snowball, as hard as he could, in the direction of the stand of trees.

He ducked down again. Another snowball whizzed through the air at them. Quickly, he made another snowball. A few feet away, he could hear both Krista and Anna sobbing.

"Well?" Ike asked Harald angrily. "Aren't you going to make any snowballs? Aren't you going to fight back?" He stared at Harald. Then Ike stood up again and threw another snowball.

He crouched back down. By now, Harald was almost curled up in a little ball. His hands covered his face.

"Aren't you going to help?" Ike asked him. Then he stopped. "Or are you the one who set this up?" he snapped. Ike knew the answer.

Hadn't Harald tried to make them late this morning? That gave the ambusher plenty of time to make snowballs and hide in the trees before they got there. Plus, wasn't Harald the only one who hadn't gotten hit?

Ike felt his anger rise. He wanted to reach out, grab Harald by the collar, and pound his ugly face into the snow. But he couldn't. He just couldn't let Father down again.

Instead, Ike scooped up some more snow. He squeezed it together as hard as he could. Then Ike jumped up and hurled the snowball.

Whoever it was ran out of the trees toward the school. Ike stared at the boy's back. Red hair peeked out from under his stocking cap. Rolf Bohn. It was Rolf. Figures, Ike thought.

Rolf had done everything he could to make Ike's life miserable for the last month. He made rude comments. He spilled ink on Ike's papers. "An accident," Rolf said. Ike was almost positive Rolf hid his homework once too.

Through it all, Ike had worked hard to control himself. He wanted Father's respect. But this was the limit.

"Get up!" he barked at Harald. He had to stop himself from yanking Harald onto his feet.

"Come on, girls," Ike called to Krista and Anna. "Whoever it is—" he stared at Harald " is gone now. Let's go. We'll be late to school."

Ike fumed as he trudged through the snow. He would have a little talk with Rolf about this. But he would do his talking with his fists this time. Imagine picking on little girls. What a coward. Picking on *him* was fine. *He* could take it. But not Anna—or even that brat, Krista.

And then there was Harald. He'd get Rolf to rat on Harald. Then he'd take care of Harald somehow. Ike knew he'd have to be careful though. Aunt Mary's threat from a month ago still rang in his ears.

They reached the school yard. Miss Peterson stood on the steps. She was ringing the bell. The last children hurried up the steps. Ike, Anna, Krista, and Harald followed them.

They walked into the coal room and began hanging up their coats. Darn, Ike thought. Rolf had already hung up his jacket. He was already in the classroom. Ike would have to wait until morning recess to corner him.

As soon as Ike sat down, he stared at Rolf. Rolf was smirking at him. Ike narrowed his eyes and doubled his hand into a fist. Then he mouthed the word "Wait!"

Rolf shrugged and made a face. Then he turned to face Miss Peterson.

The morning dragged. Would it ever be recess? Ike kept glaring at Rolf. Rolf just sneered at him.

"All right, boys and girls," Miss Peterson called. "You may go out for a morning break."

The students rushed into the coal room. Chatter and laughter filled the air. The schoolhouse door slammed behind each little group running outside. Feet clattered down the wooden steps.

Rolf had already gone outside. Ike buttoned his jacket. His anger was building as he thought about the ambush. He walked outside and stood at the top of the steps. He caught a flash of red hair over by the end of the yard. There he was! Rolf was playing catch near the trees.

Ike ran down the steps. He hoped Miss Peterson wasn't paying attention. Ike walked around a tree to surprise Rolf. Rolf was getting ready to throw a ball to another boy when Ike grabbed his arm.

The ball dropped onto the snow. Ike whipped Rolf around to face him. Then Ike pushed him. He doubled up his fists.

"I'm gonna teach *you* to pick on little kids," he threatened. "With rocks inside too!" Ike drew his fist back, ready to punch Rolf.

Rolf's face suddenly crumpled. "I—I—I'm sorry!" he whined. "Don't hit me, please?"

Stunned, Ike dropped his fist. What was this? A cry-baby?

"Please?" Rolf begged again. "P—please don't hit me!"

Ike shook his head. "You crybaby," he sneered. Then he stared at Rolf. "Whose idea was it?" he asked. "Harald's?"

Ike waited for Rolf to answer yes. Rolf was the type to rat on someone. He would never take the blame all himself.

"N—n—no one!" Rolf blubbered, still staring at Ike's fist. "I swear. I just thought it would be funny!"

Ike stood still. "Harald had nothing to do with this?" he asked. He couldn't believe it. It wasn't possible. "Harald didn't tell you to ambush us?"

"N—n—no!" Rolf sniveled. He reached one hand up and wiped his nose. "I—I'll never do it again, I promise," he whined.

Ike shook his head. Good thing he hadn't punched Harald back by the barn. He would have been in big trouble then. He would have hit Harald for no reason. That was even worse than hitting him for a *good* reason.

Ike looked at Rolf. He narrowed his eyes. "Fine," Ike said. He let go of Rolf.

Rolf hustled back to where he was playing catch. But

from the corner of his eye, Ike saw Rolf glare at him. His eyes were furious. Huh, Ike thought. So much for promises. Maybe Rolf wouldn't ambush him again. But it would be just a matter of time before he would think of something else to do. Ike could see that.

He had almost punched Harald. His whole family could have suffered because of his mistake. He really had to watch his temper. But how much longer could he control it?

6

Harald Opens His Mouth

Supper was over. Ike and Harald sat at the kitchen table doing their lessons. The kerosene lamp cast a golden glow over the table. Ike looked up from his history lesson. He stared at the lamp's bright flame.

He couldn't believe they didn't have electricity on the farm. He sighed. And no indoor plumbing either. It was getting pretty cold in the mornings too. He sure missed living in town. And he hated living with his cousins. When *would* his father find a job?

Ike turned to look at Krista and Anna. They were standing at the sink washing the dishes. First, they had pumped the water. Then they had heated the water on the stove.

Ike watched as Krista handed Anna a plate to dry. Just at the last minute, Krista jerked the plate away. "Don't drop it, clumsy!" she laughed. Then she held the plate out to Anna again.

Anna took the plate. She bit her lip to hold back the tears.

Ike sighed. If only Anna weren't so easy to tease. Plus, Krista was two years older. That made a difference.

Ike wished he could help Anna get back at Krista someway. In fact, he'd love to find a way to get back at *both* Harald and Krista. He grinned. Wouldn't it be great to plan something tricky? Then Ike frowned. He had to stay out of trouble though. He and Anna would just have to put up with their farm cousins.

Ike glanced at his cousin. Harald was doing his arithmetic. He was breathing noisily with his mouth open.

Almost every night, Harald woke Ike up with his snoring. Ike would get out of bed. Then he'd shake Harald. Harald's eyes would pop open in fright. "Stop snoring, you fool!" Ike would growl. Harald would roll over and drop off to sleep. In the morning, Harald never remembered anything.

Father and Uncle Jens sat in chairs by the darkened window. Uncle Jens was doing the farm records. He entered numbers in columns.

Father read farmers' magazines. The light from the

kerosene lamp on the small table cast shadows on his face. Father was looking a lot older. Not having a job was very hard on him.

Uncle Jens sighed. He looked up from his figuring.

"I don't know, Nils," he said to Father. His forehead was creased with worry. "The tractor engine needs to be overhauled. It's been sputtering. Ole Tollerud at the John Deere place can do it. But it will cost a pretty penny."

Father looked at Uncle Jens. He opened his mouth to say something.

But Uncle Jens went on. "I was planning on paying for it this winter. But then we had the dust storms. I lost crops. Money is tight." He sighed. "I'm handy with machinery. But a tractor engine overhaul is a bit beyond me."

Father looked thoughtful. He put his farm journal down. "Let me take a look at it, Jens," he said. "Maybe I can do it. I used to do all the work on the machinery and cars for the high school. Growing up on my family farm, I learned a lot from my father." He waited for Uncle Jens' answer.

Ike saw Harald look up from his work. Harald watched the two men.

"Ja, that would be good," Uncle Jens said. "Maybe tomorrow. Don't worry if you can't do it. I was going to pay to have it done anyway."

The two men went back to their reading. Ike saw a little smirk curl the corners of Harald's mouth. Ike wondered what the little brat was up to now.

Mother and Aunt Mary came in. They had been sewing in the spare room.

"Time for bed, children," Aunt Mary said. "Early to bed, early to rise…"

"Mother!" Harald complained. "You always say that."

Aunt Mary smiled at him. Why doesn't she ever get mad at him? Ike wondered. She acted like Harald could do no wrong.

Ike tapped his pencil on his book in frustration. If Aunt Mary only knew even half the stuff Harald did and said. But Ike had taught himself to stay calm. He didn't let Harald see that he was angry. As a result, Harald didn't seem to think it was so much fun any more to tease Ike. Father was right about that anyway.

It was hard not to get mad though. Especially when Harald said something about Father.

Ike bundled up his books and papers. Harald did the same. The girls stopped their bickering and put the last dishes away. Then Krista and Anna disappeared down the hall toward their bedroom.

Uncle Jens got up. He walked over to the sink. He began washing the ink off his hands. Harald and Ike walked to the doorway.

"Uncle Nils couldn't fix a broken anything," Harald hissed to Ike under his breath. "If he's so good at fixing, why did he lose his job?" He leered at Ike.

Ike tightened his mouth. "Shut up, you idiot," he hissed back.

Ike looked back into the kitchen. Aunt Mary and Mother were going over recipes at the kitchen table. Uncle Jens was drying his hands. Father was buried in his reading. Ike frowned. No one ever heard what Harald said. What a sneak! He always got away with everything.

Ike followed Harald down the hall. Just wait until Father got a job in town. Then they could move back to Great Rock. He'd make Harald wish he'd never *had* a cousin.

Aunt Mary would call him a bully, but so what? Uncle Jens couldn't kick them out. They'd already be gone.

Ike could almost taste the sweetness of victory over Harald. He couldn't wait. But for now, he—

"Harald!" Uncle Jens' voice thundered down the hall.

Harald's face drained of color.

"Ja, Father," Harald answered.

"Come here," Uncle Jens commanded.

Harald walked slowly back down the hall to the kitchen.

"You apologize to your Uncle Nils," Uncle Jens' voice barked. "I heard your rude remark. We are family. You stick by your family. You never talk like that. Do you understand?"

Ike stood in the hall. His heart raced. He couldn't believe his ears. Harald was actually in trouble!

"Y—y—yes, Father," Harald mumbled.

"Say you are sorry. Say it loud and clear—*hoyt og tidlick!*" Uncle Jens said.

Ike blinked. He hardly ever heard Uncle Jens speak Norwegian. Most everyone they knew—or their parents—had come from Sweden or Norway. But not many people spoke the old languages anymore. They all tried to speak English.

When people got angry, though, sometimes they would slip into Norwegian. Or when they were really happy. Whew! Uncle Jens must be pretty mad!

"I—I'm so—sorry, Uncle Nils," Harald stammered.

How Ike wished he could sneak around the corner! He wanted to watch this!

"Now, tell him what you are sorry *for*, my boy," Uncle Jens' voice echoed down the hall.

"Jens, please—" Aunt Mary's voice begged.

"Mary! You do not know what the boy said!" Uncle Jens said forcefully.

"I—I'm sorry I said you couldn't fix anything," Harald began to whimper.

"Yes, *and*—" Uncle Jens prompted.

"And—and no wonder y—you lost your job," Harald finished miserably. His voice trailed off.

"Harald!" Aunt Mary said. "I'm surprised at you!"

"It's all right," Father said calmly. "Boys will say things they don't mean. Sometimes they do it just to try it out. I accept your apology," he said.

"Harald," Uncle Jens' voice echoed down the hall. "We're going out behind the summer kitchen."

"No!" Harald squeaked. "Please? I'm sorry!"

Hah! Ike wanted to jump up and down and yell! Uncle Jens was going to whip Harald!

The summer kitchen was a small shed near the house with a stove in it. In the summer, it was too hot to cook in the house on the huge stove. So Aunt Mary cooked in the summer kitchen instead.

"I have told you about the importance of respecting the family," Uncle Jens said. "Now you will remember it." The back door slammed.

Later, Harald came into the bedroom. His face was red and tear-streaked. Still Harald glared at Ike.

"I don't care!" Harald whispered angrily at Ike. "I'll say what I want. Your father couldn't get a job if his life depended on it."

Ike clenched his fists under the covers. Stay calm, he told himself. Stay calm.

Harald threw back the covers on his bed. Then he turned and stared at Ike again.

"I'm really gonna get you back for this," he said.

7

Father's Job

On the way to school the next morning, Ike watched Harald carefully. He was sure Harald would be up to something. Especially after the threat last night. But they arrived at school and nothing had happened.

Maybe Harald would pull something during recess. Ike played catch with his new friends, Ray and William. He watched Harald. But still nothing happened. During late morning lessons, everything was quiet too.

At lunchtime, Harald sat with Rolf, as usual. They huddled at the back of the classroom.

Ike sat with his friends. They laughed and talked. Ike could still hear Harald's bratty voice across the room.

"Ja, ja!" Harald crowed.

Ike jerked his head around. He looked at Rolf and Harald.

They had their heads together. Rolf said something. Then Harald threw his head back and laughed.

"Great idea!" he said, grinning. Then he shook Rolf's hand.

Rolf grinned back. "I knew you'd like it," he said to Harald.

Rolf looked up to see Ike watching them. He smirked and nudged Harald.

Harald made a face. Then he narrowed his eyes at Ike.

Ike shook his head in disgust. What a couple of numbskulls.

"What are those two up to?" Ray asked.

Ike shrugged his shoulders. "Who knows?" he said. He popped the rest of his sandwich in his mouth. "No good, probably."

"Ja," Ray said, disgustedly. "That Rolf is no good." Then he grinned. "You ever want to make him *really* mad, call him a red-headed pimple!" His eyes gleamed with mischief.

Ike almost choked on his sandwich. "Red-headed pimple!" he gasped with laughter. "That's a good one!" He looked over at Rolf. He *did* sort of look like one. Ike snickered to himself.

Ike continued to watch Harald and Rolf closely. Still nothing happened.

Ike's guard was up on the way home. He made Harald walk in front of him. Krista and Anna followed behind him. Would Rolf ambush them again? Would Harald really set him up this time? But the walk home was quiet, except for Krista's and Anna's chatter.

Father was waiting for them at the back door. He was smiling.

"Well, children," he said. "I have good news." He helped Anna take off her coat.

"What, Father?" Ike asked. His heart raced under his shirt. Father had a job! It must be! Oh, please, he begged silently.

"Ole Tollerud has offered me a job at the John Deere place!" Father said. "His man just quit today. I was in the store buying some parts for the tractor. I asked for the job on the spot! He will talk with his wife tonight. If she agrees, I'll start tomorrow!" Father folded his arms and leaned against the sink. He smiled a broad smile at Ike and Anna.

Ike grinned. He wanted to hug Father—but Johnson men didn't hug each other.

"We can move back to town!" Ike exclaimed. "I can see my friends! I can go back to my school!"

All the trouble of the last month evaporated. Things would be great again! No more Harald. No more Rolf. No more of Aunt Mary's remarks. No more milking cows every morning and every afternoon. No more farm chores!

He'd get electric lights again! And indoor plumbing! And his own room! Ike wanted to jump up on the table and shout.

Mother walked into the kitchen. She smiled at them. She walked over to Father and stood next to him.

"Oh, Mother," Anna said. "I get to see my teacher again!" Then her mouth drooped. "But I'll miss Miss Peterson. She is so nice."

Miss Peterson *was* nice. Ike hadn't thought about that. He suddenly realized that he hadn't gotten into any fights at school. Miss Peterson understood when he might be angry. She listened to him. He realized he would miss her too.

"Should we start packing?" Ike asked. The sooner he was out of Harald's room, the better. He looked at Mother's and Father's happy faces.

"Maybe not," Mother said. A small worry line creased her forehead. "We don't know for sure. These days, it's better not to count on anything." She looked at Father. "Except for family, of course."

"Ja, your mother's right," Father agreed. He sighed. "Tollerud is a good man. He will be fair with me. But he has to talk with his wife. You never know what might come up," he said. "He will call tonight. "

Anna began to dance around the kitchen table. "We're going home! We're going home!" she sang. She bumped into the table leg and giggled.

Home, Ike thought. But where was home?

"Father?" Ike asked. "Where will we live?" Ike thought about their old house. If only they could go back there.

"Not to worry," Father said. "When Tollerud told me, I hurried to see Old Man Palmquist. Our old landlord, remember?"

Ike nodded. He had been a nice old gentleman. He had been sorry to see Ike and his family leave.

"He hasn't rented our little house yet," said Father.

No one was moving into Great Rock these days. Everyone was moving out of town. They hoped things would be better somewhere else. Some people were even moving to California. The Depression had hit everyone hard.

"So we can live in our old house?" Anna cried. Her eyes shone. "Everything will be the same!" She jumped up and down in delight.

Ike smiled. This was almost too good to be true. As soon as Mr. Tollerud called, Ike would start packing. And tonight, he would do his chores for the last time.

The sound of knocking at the kitchen door interrupted Ike's thoughts.

Ike's father frowned as he looked out the window. He shook his head and sighed. Then he opened the door.

A shabbily dressed man stood there. He scrunched his hat in his hands. His clothes hung loosely on him.

"Afternoon, sir," the man said. His eyes were pleading.

"Good afternoon," Nils said.

"Sorry to bother you, but I was wondering if you had any work—something I could help you with. You see, we haven't eaten for…" the man said.

Nils looked beyond the man. Ike followed his gaze. There in the yard was a rattletrap old car. He could see two small children. Ike felt his stomach churn.

"Say no more. First, we'll talk food. Then, we'll talk work." Nils said. He turned to Ike's mother. "Lillie, there are children—two."

A cloud crossed her face. "Ja," she said. She heaped three plates. Without a word, she handed two to Father and the third to Ike. Together the three walked to the old car.

"Thank you! Thank you!" the man said.

"Enjoy your dinner. And take your time," Father said. "We'll talk later about work."

The children's eyes widened when they saw the food. Ike felt a pang. He was so lucky. With all his complaining about Harald and Krista, he was still lucky. And now Father might even have a job!

Later that night, Ike and Harald milked the cows before dinner. Then they walked silently back up to the house. Ever since he had heard about Father's job, Harald had said nothing.

Hah, Ike thought. Now Harald wouldn't be able to get back at him. Ike hid a smile. Too bad for Harald.

And too bad for Rolf. Whatever the two of them had

been planning, now it didn't matter.

Harald went on through the kitchen and back to his room. Ike stayed in the little mudroom off the kitchen. He was cleaning the rest of the mud from his boots.

"Well, I, for one, am glad." Ike heard Aunt Mary's voice in the kitchen. He froze. He could imagine what was coming next.

"I can't wait to get that Ike out of here," Aunt Mary went on.

Ike tightened his mouth. She really didn't understand, did she?

"Mary, watch your tongue," Uncle Jens' voice rumbled.

"Well, I mean it. Poor Harald has just been pushed to his limit," Aunt Mary said. Pans rattled in the background, making it hard for Ike to hear. He let his breath out and squatted down to listen.

"I think too often Harald makes his own trouble," Uncle Jens said. "Like those nasty things he said about Nils not having a job." he asked. "What about that, eh?"

"Well, the poor boy was just bullied into it," Aunt Mary said. "That Ike just badgers him. Finally poor Harald explodes. You can't blame him." Ike heard wood clanking down into the iron stove.

Ike could feel his blood rushing to his forehead. Aunt Mary was crazy. She had no idea what was happening! How could she think for one minute that Harald was innocent? He almost exploded through the door into the kitchen.

Stop it, Ike, he commanded himself. He forced himself to sit still.

"Well, at least," Aunt Mary went on, "we'll have a little money again. Harald and Krista have been asking for things. I hate having to always tell them no. The Depression is bad enough. We've had a hard year, losing the crops and all. But they know it's really because Nils, Lillie, and the children are here." Aunt Mary stopped for a moment. "You can't expect Harald and Krista to be happy the family is here, can you?"

"Mary, no wonder they're not happy. Listen to you!" Uncle Jens sounded angry. "Family is important. Nils and Lillie would help us if the tables were turned. You will be gracious. I insist," he said, sternly.

Aunt Mary sighed. "Yes, Jens. I'm sorry. You're right." Ike heard more pots and pans clanking. "I'm glad we can offer them a place to stay. I know they would do the same for us. But, still, I hope they can leave soon. It's hard on everyone."

Ike scowled. Aunt Mary wasn't the only one. He hoped they could leave soon too. Now more than ever.

8

No New Skates?

The Johnsons and Mogrens sat eating supper. No one had much to say.

Ring! Ring! Ring! Ike looked up from his plate. The telephone hardly ever rang. People used it only for important times.

Three rings meant it was for the Mogrens. Several families were on the same line out here in the country. Aunt Mary had scolded Ike once for picking up the phone when it rang twice. "That's not our ring," she had said.

Aunt Mary looked at Uncle Jens across the supper table. Then she looked at Father.

Ike thought this must be the phone call about the job. This could mean freedom!

Uncle Jens nodded to Father. "Go ahead, Nils. It must be your call."

Ike watched as his father pushed his chair away from the table, walked over to the telephone, and picked up the receiver. Everyone at the supper table watched in silence.

"Mogrens'. Nils Johnson speaking," Father said. "Yes? Hello." Father turned to face the other direction. "Yes...I see...No, I understand," he said heavily.

Father's shoulders slumped. No! This couldn't be! What had happened?

"All right...Yes...Thank you. Good-bye," Father said. He hung up the receiver. Father turned around. His face looked tired.

Father walked back to the table. He sat down heavily. Mother reached out and touched his arm.

Aunt Mary looked unhappy. Uncle Jens looked concerned. Ike couldn't read Harald's expression. What was he thinking?

Father spoke. "Well, as you could probably tell, I didn't get the job." He stared at his plate.

"Oh, no!" Anna blurted out. Tears filled her eyes.

"I don't understand, Nils," Uncle Jens said. "You are a good mechanic. You have the tractor almost up and running after only two days." Uncle Jens frowned. "Tollerud must be crazy not to hire you."

"He gave the job to his wife's cousin, Sven. Sven got laid off in Fargo. He needed a job. So family came first," Father sighed. "I can understand that."

"You'll find something," Mother said firmly.

"Ja," Father said. He didn't sound convincing though.

"Well, it's Tollerud's loss and our gain," Uncle Jens said. He nodded. "I had a harder time running this place without you. I don't know how I did it before. You're a real help. That's for sure, ja," he said.

Ike was watching Aunt Mary. She was frowning. She was probably thinking how they'd all have to put up with the Johnson family even longer.

The two families finished supper in silence. Silverware clinked. Plates rattled. But no one said anything. Ike glanced at Harald out of the corner of his eye.

Once, Harald smirked at him. Ike narrowed his eyes and stared back in anger. Harald quickly looked down at his plate.

Ike clenched his fists as he lay in bed that night. He was just waiting for Harald to open his fat mouth.

"So!" Harald began after he put out the lamp. "No job for the old man, eh?"

Ike lay silent. He could barely control his fury. He hardly dared to breathe.

"Too bad," Harald sneered. "I knew no one would hire him. Everyone knows he's a loser. The worst part is now we still have to have you here."

Ike thought the top of his head would blow right off. He was furious. Still, he was not going to let Harald get to him.

Before too long, Ike heard Harald's raspy snores. But Ike was too angry to relax. He lay awake for a long time before he dropped off to sleep.

The walk to school the next morning was quiet. As Ike opened the door of the schoolhouse, he thought about his father's failed job. He'd thought that he'd never have to come back. But here he was again.

And now he'd have to put up with Harald and Rolf all day long. Ike frowned. Well, he could handle them. He'd just have to be on his guard.

Ike helped Anna with her coat.

"Anna, come see," Ingrid Ellefson said. She smiled at Anna. "I have something to show you."

Eagerly, Anna joined Ingrid at her desk. They chattered happily.

Krista frowned at them. Ingrid had always been Krista's friend. And it didn't look like she wanted to share her. Krista marched over to Ingrid's desk.

She pushed herself between Ingrid and Anna. "Want to play a new game at recess, Ingrid?" she asked.

Anna's head drooped. Ingrid looked past Krista at Anna. Then she looked at Krista.

"Ja, sure. If Anna can play too," Ingrid said. She smiled at Anna.

Anna smiled back. Krista stuck out her lower lip.

"Fine," she muttered. She stomped off to her desk.

Ike grinned to himself. He sat down at his wooden desk. Miss Peterson was straightening papers on her desk. It was almost time for school to start.

Behind him, he could hear Rolf call to Harald.

"Hey!" Rolf whispered loudly. "Hey, Mogren!"

"Ja?" Harald answered. "What do you want?"

"Ice is getting thicker on the pond. Did you get your new skates yet?" Rolf asked.

Harald didn't answer. Ike turned around to see Harald pointing at him.

"No new skates," Harald said. "I got a cousin instead." He made a face.

Ike tightened his mouth. He felt his face turn warm above his collar. Great, he thought. Now it was *his* fault Harald didn't get new skates.

He remembered what Aunt Mary had said. "The children can't get new things," she had told Uncle Jens. Because he and his family were staying with the Mogrens, there was no money for Harald's new skates.

"Ohhhh," Rolf jeered. "No new skates for Harald. Too bad," he said. "Well, I'm going skating at Hansen's pond Saturday. It'll sure be a lot of fun. But, I guess *you* can't go," he added.

Ike turned so he could catch a glimpse of Rolf's face. He was grinning wickedly at Harald. What a jerk, Ike thought. He was even rude with his own friends.

"I can go," Harald said slowly. "My old ones probably still fit."

"Huh!" Rolf said. "Too bad you can't have new skates. Too bad. But what a nice cousin you got instead!" he leered.

Ike had mixed feelings. He wanted to pound Rolf, but he felt bad for Harald too. But why? he asked himself. Harald had been nothing but mean to him.

"Shut up," Harald hissed to Rolf. "You red-headed pimple!"

Ike hid a smile. Hah! he thought. So even the two friends had fights.

"Children, time to begin the day," Miss Peterson called. Ike straightened up. Well, maybe it was good they were mad at each other. Then maybe they'll leave me alone, Ike thought.

Ike sighed. No chance, he thought glumly. Rolf and Harald would be friends again by the end of the day. They'd have plenty of time to make their plans.

Harald *had* threatened him, after all. "You're gonna pay for this," Harald had said after the whipping. And now Ike was also the reason Harald had no new skates.

9
Who Did It?

The four children walked home from school as usual. Krista and Anna chattered away. Sure! Ike snorted to himself. Krista's friends were being nice to Anna at school. So Krista had no choice but to be nice to her too.

After their chores were finished, Harald disappeared. Ike thought he saw him rushing across the yard carrying something in a sack.

Harald came home, much later, puffing and out of breath. He said nothing to Ike, but he looked very pleased with himself.

Ike watched Harald all through dinner and bedtime. Every now and then, Harald had a little smile on his face. Ike knew that Harald had been up to something. He and Rolf had probably gotten together. They were definitely planning something. But what?

The next morning, Aunt Mary and Mother finished packing their lunches. "I hope you enjoy the sandwiches," Aunt Mary said to the boys. "Anna helped me bake the bread." Anna blushed.

Ike glanced at Krista, who was looking down at the floor. She hadn't even helped her own mother. What a spoiled brat.

The four children crunched through the snow on their way to school. The weak winter sun shone in a pale blue sky. Last night's snow had colored everything white. The world looked fresh and clean.

As the four approached the schoolhouse, they could see a group of children standing in front of the steps. Usually, everyone was running or standing around in the yard. Not this morning. They were all discussing something. Their voices carried across the snowy fields. What was happening?

Ingrid Ellefson rushed up to Krista and Anna. Her eyes were wide with excitement.

"Guess what? Guess what?" she cried. "The girls' outhouse! Someone pushed it over! And Miss Peterson is really mad!"

Ike's heart sank. It didn't take him long to figure out

what was happening. Harald—and probably Rolf too—had pushed over the girls' outhouse. They would blame him.

Well, let them go ahead and blame him. He wouldn't confess to it. He didn't do it. The bad part was he couldn't beat up Harald to make him confess. He couldn't even beat up Rolf. He was determined not to disappoint Father.

The four cousins joined the students milling around the schoolhouse steps. Miss Peterson walked around the corner. She was frowning.

"All right, children," she said. Everyone quieted down. "I insist on knowing who did this." She scanned the group with her eyes. "Be honorable and own up to it."

Silence. The boys looked uncomfortably at each other. Ike watched Harald and Rolf. They were staring at each other. Rolf's neck flushed red above his jacket and scarf. It almost matched the color of his hair. Ike knew that any minute one of the two of them would blame him.

"I'll have to get Mr. Ellefson out here with a team of horses to pull it back up," Miss Peterson said. "Until then, the girls will use the boys' outhouse. Boys," she looked at them, "you're out of luck. It's the trees for you."

The boys muttered and laughed a little. Ike frowned.

"It's not funny," said Miss Peterson. "Mr. Ellefson has other things to do besides upend the girls' outhouse. It was a very inconsiderate and stupid thing to do." She looked at each of the boys in turn. "I'll have to punish all of you if no one confesses. You'll all be staying after school to copy dictionary definitions.

"Now, it's time to get down to business." With that, Miss Peterson turned and began walking up the steps. The children filed behind her.

The girls whispered together as they hurried up the steps. The boys trudged slowly behind them. They muttered to each other.

Great, Ike thought. Now they'd all have to stay after school. There were already too many chores to do after school. With such a late start, he and Harald would have to work by lantern light to get them all done.

Lessons began as usual. Just before recess, Miss Peterson quieted the class.

"So far, no one has confessed." She looked at the boys. Was it his imagination, or did she stare longer at Harald and Rolf?

"Time is running out," she warned them. Then she excused them for recess.

The students grabbed their coats and jackets. Buttoned up, they scattered to the school yard.

Ike, Ray, and William threw a baseball around. As they played, Ike scanned the school yard. He didn't see Rolf's red hair anywhere.

Ike missed a throw and turned around to chase it. He looked up. There, coming down the steps, was Rolf. Miss Peterson was behind him. She held her head high. Her back was straight. Her mouth was set in a thin line.

Ike picked up the ball and threw it to Ray. Had Rolf

been talking to Miss Peterson about the outhouse? She looked really mad.

Ike caught a throw from William. Wait! he thought. What if Rolf told Miss Peterson *Ike* had done it? Ike whipped around. Was Miss Peterson coming to talk to *him?*

How could he get out of this one? His mother and father would be disappointed. So would Uncle Jens. Aunt Mary would say she wasn't surprised. His body was tense as he gripped the ball tightly and waited.

Miss Peterson marched across the school yard. But she stopped in front of Harald.

Ike saw that Rolf hung back. He hadn't followed Miss Peterson. Rolf shoved his hands in his pockets. He stared at the snowy ground. What was going on?

"Harald Mogren!" Miss Peterson's voice snapped. She put her hands on her hips. Her eyes blazed with anger.

"Yes, Miss Peterson?" Harald answered. Color drained from his face.

"Is there something you want to tell me?" Miss Peterson demanded. "You have put your entire class in jeopardy. They all stand to be punished because of you. For your selfish act."

Harald's jaw dropped. "Miss Peterson!" he exclaimed. "You don't think *I* pushed over the outhouse, do you? I didn't do it! Honest, I didn't!" His eyes shifted from side to side. "Why do you think *I* did it?" he asked.

Everyone in the school yard had stopped to watch the little drama. Harald?! Ike couldn't believe his ears. Rolf had tattled on Harald, not him? Whew, Ike thought in amazement.

Harald was in trouble now. Too bad. Sneaky Harald probably thought he could get away with it. Now both Rolf and Harald would be punished. Unless, of course, Harald had done it all alone.

Ike hid a smile. This was almost worth all the taunting and teasing he had been forced to put up with.

Harald would be in big trouble at home too! Wouldn't Aunt Mary be stunned to learn the truth? Her precious boy was a prankster and a cheat. And Uncle Jens would get out the belt and take Harald behind the summer kitchen again. This would be too good to miss.

Harald was beginning to shake now. "N— n —no, Miss Peterson. I swear on a stack of Bibles. I didn't do it." He looked around the school yard. Then he spied Rolf standing by a tree. Harald pointed at Rolf.

"There!" he said loudly. "Rolf did it! *He's* the one!"

Everyone turned to look at Rolf. Rolf's face turned the color of his hair.

"No!" Rolf shouted. "I didn't!" He stamped his foot in the snow. "I didn't! That liar Mogren did it!"

Miss Peterson frowned at Harald. Then she turned to glare at Rolf.

"You two have until the end of recess to work this out. You decide who did it. I want to hear from one of you by the time recess is over." She gave both boys an icy stare. Then she walked back to the steps and into the schoolhouse.

Harald looked at Ike. Ike turned around and began playing catch with Ray and William again. The next thing he knew, Harald tapped him on the shoulder. Ike sighed and turned around.

"I need to talk to you," Harald whispered. His eyes pleaded with Ike.

"What about?" Ike asked. "Want *me* to confess for you, you little idiot?"

"I—I didn't do it! I swear!" Harald said. His eyes were wide with fear.

And with good cause, Ike thought. Another whipping behind the summer kitchen would be no joke.

"Ja, sure," Ike mocked him. "And you just went out for a walk yesterday afternoon." He narrowed his eyes at Harald. "I saw you sneak away from the house. You went to the school and pushed over the outhouse!" he accused. "You were probably going to blame it on me too!"

Harald stared at him. "No!" he said. "I mean, yes, I did go out. But I went to try out my old skates on Hansen's pond. I wanted to see if they still fit. Please, you have to believe me!" He stopped. "You have to help me! I need your help! *Please?*" he begged.

10

Family Sticks Together

"Why should I help you?" Ike snapped at Harald. He slammed the ball into the palm of his hand. "All you've done is make fun of me. You've said rude things about my father. I don't owe you anything."

Ike turned his back on Harald. He threw the ball to Ray.

"Listen, please," Harald begged again. "I—I'm sorry, all right? I am. Really." He shook Ike's shoulder.

"Don't touch me," Ike barked at him. "I don't care if you are sorry. It's too late now. You should have thought of that a month ago. You deserve everything you're going to get. And you're gonna get plenty!" Ike added.

Harald lowered his head. He turned and walked away. Serves him right, Ike thought. Let him pay for it. He caught Ray's throw and threw the ball to William.

Even though he tried to ignore it, a thought nagged at Ike. What if Harald *was* telling the truth. Was it possible? "Throw with William for a while," he told Ray.

Ike walked over to a tree. He leaned back against the smooth bark. He put his hands in his pockets. Thinking was what he needed to do right now.

Harald *had* been carrying a bag yesterday. Maybe his old skates had been inside it. Also Harald *had* seemed happy all during supper. Knowing that he could skate with all his friends during the winter would make him happy. Without skates, he would be out of a lot of fun.

Ike scowled. If he could be sure Harald was telling the truth, he should do something to help him. It was fine for Harald to get in trouble. He usually deserved it. But not for something he didn't do.

There was just one way to find out if Rolf was lying. He'd threaten Rolf with a beating. That coward Rolf would confess right away. Ike snorted.

Ike stood up. He took a deep breath. Recess was almost over. He saw Rolf lounging against the railing of the schoolhouse steps. Ike put his shoulders back and walked toward Rolf.

Rolf started. He blinked his eyes rapidly. "Wha— what do you want?" he stuttered.

"You liar," Ike said in a low voice. He looked around to make sure Miss Peterson wasn't listening. "You weakling."

"I—I—I don't know what you mean!" Rolf said. He began to turn white. His freckles stood out on his face.

Ike sneered. "You pushed over the outhouse, you little liar. You did it! And you—" Ike jabbed a finger into Rolf's chest, "think you're gonna get away with it!"

"Y—you're crazy!" Rolf stammered. His eyes shifted from side to side.

"You can't blame a Mogren for something *you* did, you cheat!" Ike exclaimed. He jabbed harder. "And if you don't tell Miss Peterson the truth, I'm gonna take care of you after school." Ike put his face in Rolf's face. "I'm gonna tear your heart out and pull it out right up through your nostrils!"

"O—okay!" Rolf bleated. He looked terrified. "I—I did it. All by myself." He shook a little. "But," he said, "it was Harald's idea. We were gonna blame you," he said defiantly.

So that had been their plan. Ike was right. They had been up to something.

"It doesn't matter whose idea it was. You did it. And you've got some explaining to do." he said. He stared at Rolf from under lowered eyebrows. "Or else…"

"O—okay, okay," Rolf said. He hurried up the school house steps.

Harald had thanked Ike after school. Then he had

lowered his eyes and quickly walked home alone.

Ike was still disgusted that Rolf and Harald had planned to get him into trouble. But the way things turned out, it didn't matter. And at least now Ike didn't have to feel bad about Harald's skates.

Later, the family sat around the supper table.

"Ja," Uncle Jens was saying. "The tractor is all ready for spring now. Thanks to you, Nils," he said, looking at Father with a smile. "Mary," he said, turning to Aunt Mary, "Nils has even found some new planting ideas in the farm journals."

Uncle Jens turned back to Father. "I'm wondering now how I ever ran the farm without your help. I hope…"

Ring! Ring! Ring! Ike's fork froze in midair, halfway to his mouth.

Mother looked at Father. Father looked up from his plate.

Aunt Mary got up and took the receiver off the hook. "Mogrens'," she said. "Ja. Ja, he is," she said. She looked at Father. "For you," she said, holding out the phone. Father pushed his chair away from the table. He took the phone from Aunt Mary.

"Ja? Nils Johnson here," he said into the receiver.

Was it about a job? What if it was another chance to move into town? Ike thought about leaving Ray and William. Skating all winter with his new friends sounded fun. And Miss Peterson? He liked having her for his teacher. Even Anna had made friends. And she and Krista

74

were getting along. Then Ike looked over at Harald. He frowned.

"Well, I will see. Ja, thank you." Father hung up the phone and came back to the table.

"Father!" Anna said. "Who was that? Are we moving back?" she asked.

"It was Ole Tollerud," Father said, looking at everyone. "His wife's cousin found another job in Fargo. He decided to stay there instead. So I can have the job after all. We can move back to town."

Mother looked thoughtful. Aunt Mary looked at Uncle Jens.

"You know, Nils," Uncle Jens said. "I've been thinking." He looked at Aunt Mary. "Mary and I have been talking too." He stopped. "If—if you would be willing to stay and help me work the farm, we have an idea."

Stay? Ike thought. They might stay?

"I'm sure we'll make more money on the farm with all your help. Your ideas are worth a lot. We'll grow more crops. And you can fix things. You saved us a lot of money on the tractor.

"We thought we could build another house on the farm. It would be yours, Nils and Lillie, your own." Uncle Jens sighed. "I would—we all would like you to stay and be a family."

Ike sat still. He couldn't believe it. They would have their own house? They'd never had that. And Uncle Jens and Aunt Mary thought Father was important for the farm too. Ike looked at his father's rough hands. Father would have a job. He would be proud again.

Ike looked at Harald and Krista. He couldn't tell what they were thinking. Maybe they figured that with Father's help, things would get better for them too.

Father looked at Mother and smiled. Then he turned to Uncle Jens. "Well, Lillie and I have been talking too, and ja, we will stay."

"Wonderful!" Uncle Jens said heartily. He stood up, smiling, and shook Father's hand.

Ike looked around at everyone—even Harald. Then he began to smile too. Well, this was their family, wasn't it? And he guessed they would stick together after all.